Autism: supporting your teenager

Caroline Hattersley

The National
Autistic Society

First published 2014 by The National Autistic Society
393 City Road, London EC1V 1NG
www.autism.org.uk

The National Autistic Society is a charity registered in England and Wales
(269425 and in Scotland (SC039427) and a company limited by guarantee
registered in England (No.1205298), registered office: 393 City Road, London
EC1V 1NG.

ISBN 978 1 905722 99 0

Written by **Caroline Hattersley**
Cover illustration by **Emily Jepps**
Designed by **Claire Lythgoe**
Printed by **Orchard Press Cheltenham Ltd**

This book is dedicated to the memory of valued
colleagues and friends from my time at
The National Autistic Society:
Mike Collins, Jon Dibb, Carly Groombridge
and Stephen Woollcott.

Acknowledgements

Thanks to all those young people and their families who have helped to grow my understanding over the many years I have worked in the field of autism. I hope this book may continue to help others on their journey.

In addition, my thanks go to some individuals that have supported me in writing this book. Firstly, to my husband, **Steve Reynoldson**, for being my rock. Also, to my good friend, **Dean Beadle**, whom I first met outside an Edinburgh hotel on a rainy day more than eight years ago. He has taught me so much through his friendship and support, both about myself and about being a young person growing up with autism. My thanks go to him for kindly agreeing to write the foreword. Thanks also to **Adam Walker** who helped in the early stages of planning for this book.

I'd also like to thank the dedicated staff and volunteers at **The National Autistic Society** for sharing their resources and expertise, which have all helped to shape this book.

About the author

Caroline Hattersley is the Deputy CEO of **Providence Row**, overseeing the delivery of the charity's current range of programmes as well as developing new areas of personalised and psychologically informed services for their clients. Prior to joining Providence Row Caroline spent more than eight years as Head of Information, Advice and Advocacy at The National Autistic Society.

She has worked in a range of settings with children, young people and adults with autism, other disabilities and mental health difficulties. She has been published in a number of journals and her first book, *Autism: understanding behaviour* was published in May 2013.

 Twitter: @CaroHatt

Contents

Foreword by **Dean Beadle**

The teenage years can be a challenging period in any person's life. Hormones, puberty, discovering your sexuality, hormones, peer pressure, exam stress, hormones, preparing for adulthood and did I mention hormones? When you then add being on the autism spectrum into the mix it often becomes a very complex period for not only the young person but for those supporting them too.

For me, as a person with a diagnosis of Asperger syndrome, my teenage years were a very complex time indeed. Whilst I had developed body odour I hadn't developed any desire to bath more than once a week. This meant that I wasn't the most pleasant person to sit next to during double maths on a summer's afternoon!

My teenage years were also the period when I started to think about my diagnosis. What did this mean? How would it affect my life? Gradually I grew to accept and then celebrate my diagnosis, but it was a lot to get my head around at first.

Often people on the spectrum have real difficulties when it comes to sleeping. In my case, it can affect how long it takes me to get to sleep. The hormonal changes related to adolescence can also impact on sleeping pattern, meaning that mum's task of waking me up for school in the morning became an Olympic sport!

Socially, it was also the period in which I formed my first proper, inclusive friendships, some of which have lasted to this day. Although these friendships have enriched my life, it's fair to say that socialising doesn't necessarily come naturally to me. It involves a lot of extra work on my part to observe and analyse my social performance so that I can 'get it right'. And then much later on I started to develop romantic feelings – which is another story altogether!

As my adolescence drew to a close, I was faced with the process of finding my way in the world of employment. I began work at 15 when I found myself speaking about my diagnosis at a training seminar. Since then I've spent ten years touring the UK as well as speaking at conferences and seminars in Denmark, Australia and New Zealand. I also spent six years as a freelance journalist for local, national and international publications.

Although there were numerous social and emotional challenges throughout my teenage years, I still look back on them fondly. Those years taught me all of the life skills I needed for adulthood. I discovered my individuality and became part of a strong friendship group. I built on my social understanding and boosted my confidence. See, it's not all doom and gloom!

The great joy of this book is that it isn't hundreds of pages of dry theory. It's packed with practical information and activities aimed at demystifying the teenage years. Going through adolescence can be a daunting prospect, but hopefully this book will take some of the unpredictability out of the process so that the teenage years can be as positive for you as they ultimately were for me.

Dean Beadle

Twitter: **@deanbeadleuk**
Facebook: **Dean Beadle Speaker**

Introduction

Being a teenager today is a tough gig for anyone. The pressures on our young people grow each day: pressure to conform, to succeed and achieve at school, to develop friendships, find a boyfriend or girlfriend, the list goes on and on. In addition, our young people experience other challenges – such as peer pressure and bullying – and the prospect of unemployment as they get older. Each day, more and more of our young people experience difficulties with their mental health. Depression and anxiety are common among young people who are struggling to fit into these endless expectations. The charity Young Minds quotes research showing that 80,000 young people experience severe depression, and 290,000 young people have an anxiety disorder.[1]

Being a teenager with autism can bring many challenges and as parents and carers, we want to do the best for our children. This book looks at a number of issues that teenagers experience in life and explores how autism impacts on them. It gives some practical suggestions for parents and carers to use to support their child with autism to negotiate the challenging teenage years and live a full life.

Chapter 1 explores diagnosis and suggests some ideas on how to communicate a diagnosis of autism to a young person. Chapter 2 looks at wellbeing and how we as parents and carers can support young people with autism to develop a strong sense of self-worth and resilience. Chapter 3 covers a range of areas relating to daily life, including school life, transitions, and healthy living and gives some ideas and suggestions for parents to use when supporting their child. Chapter 4 tackles the often difficult area of relationships. It looks at the challenges of puberty, sexuality and relationships. Finally, the message on page 39 invites you to think about looking after yourself so you are better able to support your child.

---

1. Young Minds (2014). *Mental health statistics*. www.youngminds.org.uk/training_services/policy/mental_health_statistics (Accessed: 16 August 2014)

This is not a 'how to' book, nor is it comprehensive. Autism affects everyone differently and, as parents and carers, the hopes we have for our children vary. Rather, this book aims to give clear and accurate information about some key areas of teenage life and how autism may impact them – and it outlines some practical strategies to help you. This book contains examples of different resources as well as links and references to help you find more information about specific issues you and your child may face. Importantly this book is based on The National Autistic Society's experiences of the many families that contact them each year for support and information.

A note on terminology

Throughout this book, the term autism is used to describe the range of diagnoses that a young person may have, including Asperger syndrome. In addition, the term 'parent' or 'parent and carer' is used to refer to all those with responsibility for supporting teenagers with autism, which might include extended family members, foster carers and others.

Using this book

Throughout this book, there are a number of activity boxes. As each young person and family is different, you can use these activities to reflect on how the particular areas discussed relate to your child. You may also like to work through these activities with other adults in your child's life, with a group of other parents of young people with autism, as a family group, including siblings or directly with your child with autism. How you use this book is up to you. Taking time to reflect on how the information presented relates directly to your child and family will help you to understand your child's unique strengths. This will enable you to support them to live a full and active life as they navigate the often difficult transition from childhood to adulthood.

Chapter 1: what is autism?

Diagnosis

There are lots of places where parents and carers can learn about autism, so in this section we will look at how parents and carers can help a young person to understand, come to terms with and even embrace their diagnosis.

Many young people with a diagnosis of autism received it when they were young children. Others are diagnosed as they enter their teenage years. In either case, young people need support to know what their diagnosis means as their understanding and awareness develops.

Getting a diagnosis is often difficult and can take a lot of time. Parents and carers have different reactions to receiving a diagnosis; relief, anger and guilt are all normal and understandable ones. Each family will come to terms with the diagnosis in their own way, Mums, dads, siblings and extended family members all have different reactions and different hopes and worries for the future. In the same way, a young person will have different feelings and reactions as they start to understand their own diagnosis.

Autism is a fairly 'modern' diagnosis, having first been defined in the 1940s. As our understanding of the human body and brain develops, so does our understanding and knowledge of autism. There are many different terms that are used to describe autism. The most common are autism, Asperger syndrome and autism spectrum disorder (ASD). In addition there are a number of terms that adults and young adults have adopted to describe themselves and others with the condition.

People with autism can have additional difficulties such as learning difficulties, physical disabilities, ADHD, mental health difficulties like anxiety, speech or language difficulties and specific learning difficulties like dyslexia to name a few.

They may also have very varied IQ levels, including some individuals with very high IQs.

These additional factors will impact on the support a young adult may need to understand their diagnosis.

Characteristics of autism

Whatever additional difficulties someone with autism may experience, we know that all people on the spectrum experience difficulties in three key areas. These are social interaction, social communication and social imagination. Many people with autism also experience sensory sensitivities.

Social interaction difficulties that young people with autism may experience include some of the following:

> making and keeping friends
> understanding the unwritten rules of behaviour
> not being sure how to respond to other people
> finding it hard to understand relationships
> struggling to understand teenage communication
> being unaware of – or obsessed with – teenage fashion trends
> not sharing the same interests as their peers
> finding the give-and-take of friendships challenging
> approaching others inappropriately or appearing 'odd'
> finding feelings of sexuality frustrating or confusing.

Social communication difficulties that a young person with autism may experience include:

> using language socially

> understanding the spoken word

> reading faces and other non-verbal communication

> preferring to be alone or avoiding social contact

> misunderstanding situations and behaving inappropriately as a result

> having difficulty in identifying other people's motives

> having difficulty processing instructions

> interrupting other people's conversations

> taking things literally

> talking incessantly about a single subject

> having difficulty understanding how teenagers converse.

Social imagination difficulties they may experience include:

> understanding what other people may be thinking or feeling

> having inflexible thoughts or being rigid in behaviour

> finding it difficult to make choices – whether small day to day choices or major life changing decisions

> preferring routine and struggling to cope with unexpected changes

> finding it difficult to organise themselves – meeting deadlines, keeping tidy and organised

> experiencing fear or anxiety when in unpredictable situations

> being obsessively interested in particular objects or subjects

> having no sense of danger

> not picking up on how others are feeling.

Young people with autism can experience sensory sensitivity in a number of different areas. These are sight, sound, smell, taste, touch (including pain and temperature awareness), balance and coordination (also called 'vestibular') and in body position awareness (also known as 'proprioception'). Difficulties might relate to young people either being under- or over-sensitive to sensory input. Reactions may also vary at different times and in different places.

Sensory difficulties may mean that a young person with autism does some of the following:

> avoids or becomes distressed by certain situations because of sensory issues such as light, smell or sounds

> avoids touch or becomes distressed when touched

> doesn't like wearing certain clothes because of the feel of them on their skin

> has a narrow or restricted diet because of finding it difficult to eat certain foods

> shows an unusual reaction to pain

> is easily distracted by surroundings

> avoids showers or washing

> dresses inappropriately for the weather

> isn't always aware of how close or far away they are standing from others and has difficulty judging distances

> has difficulty modulating their voice

> avoids sport or team games because of feeling clumsy or uncoordinated.

In addition to these problems, young people with autism may have difficulties with sleep, their diet or eating patterns, fears and phobias, tics, motivation and aggression.

Strengths and qualities

Autism brings with it many challenges but it also brings many qualities and strengths. As parents, our main job is to help our children develop a good sense of self-worth which will help them as adults to live a full and satisfying life. The more we can do as parents to build the self-esteem of our children, the more resilient they will be as they move into their adult life.

Some of the qualities that young people with autism may have include:

> a strong sense of justice
> fewer social inhibitions
> a different way of seeing the world
> attention to detail
> determination
> technical skills
> a good factual memory
> excellent knowledge in areas of interest
> honesty and openness.

The list of possibilities is endless.

Activity

Take some time to think about the following:

> What are the strengths of your son or daughter?
> What is your son or daughter interested in?
> What are your hopes for your child's future?

Explaining the diagnosis

It is important to support your son or daughter to understand their diagnosis, but the way in which you decide to do this will depend on their level of understanding. Generally, people with autism benefit from being helped to understand their diagnosis, whatever their level of understanding – but there are lots of ways to do this in a way that will help them to develop their self-worth and understand the positive qualities they have.

Many parents and carers begin to help their child to understand their diagnosis from a very young age, but there is no hard-and-fast rule about when it is best to start sharing this with a child or young person. It is worth remembering that children are often extremely sensitive to difference, and children often pick up bits of information before we think they are able to. Whenever you decide to begin this process, all children will benefit from having a basic awareness of what their diagnosis means for them. In principle, if a child is able to understand they have a right to know about their diagnosis and to start to own it as part of their identity.

Before opening these discussions it is important to consider if you are emotionally ready to share the diagnosis in a positive way. It is important to be honest with yourself about this, and if you need more time or support before brokering the discussion, then take it. Of course, some children may start to become aware of their differences and raise the question themselves. There are some simple activities you can do before or during discussions about the diagnosis in the Resources and information section (page 40) and activities like the one overleaf can help to frame these discussions in a positive way.

> ## Activity
>
> List all your family's likes, talents and difficulties on individual cards or post-it notes and go through them together guessing which belongs to each person.
>
> **Some questions to think about:**
>
> 1. Are some things the same for different people?
> 2. Can anyone's 'likes' help someone else with their difficulties? For example mum likes organising things, but dad has trouble being organised sometimes; John likes maths but Emily tends to find numbers confusing.

It is also worth thinking about who is best placed to open the discussion with your child, and who could support you with responding to difficult questions. Many professionals have experience of sharing diagnoses with children and young people and with supporting parents or carers to do this. There are many resources available that can help you as you start to think about this and some are listed at the end of this book.

As much as this will take a lot of preparation and work on your part to gather resources, your child may not show much initial interest in the discussion. This may indicate that they are not ready to take in lots of information, or just that it will take them time to make sense of what you are telling them. Keep the discussion as relaxed and informal as possible and remember that this is not a one-off conversation, try to think back to how you took time to accept and understand the diagnosis. Your child will likely feel many of the same things you did as they start to understand what it means to have autism. Some children and young people may not want to accept their diagnosis and may take many years before they are willing to talk about autism, some may never accept the diagnosis, or may simply refuse to talk about it. If they don't want to use the term, then try to support them in this, or agree to disagree and support them to understand whatever difficulties they do want to talk about as they arise.

Activity

When you are preparing to discuss a diagnosis with a child, think about the following questions:

> What is my child's level of understanding?

> Am I emotionally ready to discuss this with my child in a positive way?

> When is the best time and where is the best place to have this discussion?

> Who should be involved in the discussion?

> What kinds of questions might my child ask me? Am I ready to answer them?

> What resources could I use to support the discussion? These may include videos, story books, pictures or written information.

> Who else needs to be told about the diagnosis once my child is aware? This might be school, siblings, extended family or youth workers.

> What is my plan for responding to difficult questions or questions when I don't know the answer? For example, an agreement to find out the answer and talk about that question at another (specified) time.

> How will I help my child to tell other people if they want to share their diagnosis?

> Who can I talk to after I have had this discussion to get some support?

Explaining autism is not easy – even the professionals disagree on how to describe the condition. What is important is that your child develops an understanding of autism that is right for them. Developing a shared understanding within your family will also be helpful as together you work to navigate the difficult journey from teenager to adulthood.

Some key things to bear in mind when explaining autism are:

> use clear and straightforward language

> use resources to support you (visual, written, online) that will help your child to understand

> try to make it positive and think about strengths

> help your child to understand that it is common, and just another way of seeing the world

> the condition may make it harder to understand other people, but many people with autism do make friends and have successful relationships

> build their understanding over time – try not to overload them in one session.

The overall message we want to communicate to young people with autism is that everyone is different, and that we all have strengths and challenges. They should know that they will have difficulties but that over time and with the right support they can overcome these difficulties. A diagnosis of autism is still often treated like something that should be kept a secret that people are unwilling to discuss. It is important that young people with autism don't feel that the way they experience the world cannot be talked about. They will experience times when they get upset and wish they didn't have the condition. They have a right to know about themselves and to know that they can talk to someone if they feel sad or upset. It isn't easy, but being open and positive is a good place to start.

Chapter 2: wellbeing

Being a young person today is hard. They experience so many pressures in every area of their lives that developing a sense of wellbeing often takes a back seat.

Developing self-esteem

For young people with autism, it is vital that we help to support them to develop a strong sense of self-worth and wellbeing, as they are often at increased risk of developing anxiety, depression and other mental health issues. Research for The National Autistic Society's *You Need to Know* campaign found that over 70 per cent of young people with autism also have mental health problems.[2]

Helping a young person develop their self-esteem can be a complex task; it is difficult to measure and intangible. The development of self-worth begins from birth, starting with how those around us love and care for us, and developing as we grow up into the views and beliefs we hold about ourselves. For a child with a disability, the focus can often be on helping them to overcome the challenges they face and on the skills they need to learn. This is especially true for a child with autism. Taking time to focus on who they are and what they want from life can help to foster a sense of self-worth for the young person as they are, rather than always focusing on what they need to learn to do.

As parents, our only real job is to raise children who like themselves. If a young person has that, the rest will fall into place. That doesn't mean we should stop teaching them the skills they need, but that we should do it in a way that emphasises and builds on their strengths and their uniqueness. An important part of this is taking time to share their interests and passions. As parents, we need to recognise that who they are and the things they enjoy are important building blocks for developing a strong sense of self-esteem.

2. Madders, T. (2010). *You Need To Know*. London: The National Autistic Society

Praise and recognition are important for all children and for children and young people with autism this is especially true. Pointing out their unique gifts and skills and telling them when they do things right regularly will help them to build a positive view of themselves. Similarly if you are using rewards to reinforce particular behaviours, remember that it is important to sometimes reward them just for being themselves. Some young people with autism can find receiving praise difficult so you may need to think carefully about how you give this kind of feedback to your child.

In the last chapter, we looked at how to tell your child about their diagnosis of autism. Once they have an understanding of the condition, it can be useful to help them to identify other people with autism whom they can spend time with (perhaps from school or a youth club). In addition, reading autobiographies of people with autism, watching them online and being positive about autism culture can support young people with autism to see the range of things that others with autism have achieved. Some suggested resources are listed in the Resources and information section of this book (page 40).

As well as helping young people with autism to develop their social skills, it is also good to help them to learn how to ask for the things they need to support them. This could be asking someone to speak more slowly, giving them time to think before having to respond, or asking someone not to touch them. This can be difficult for a young person, but feeling able to ask for what they need is an important part of developing self-confidence. Another element of this may be supporting them to get feedback from others. This could be asking things like 'Let me know if I am talking too much', 'If I do something annoying, it's okay to tell me' or 'I don't like to talk much, but I am listening'.

Developing interests

Another way to develop self-esteem is by doing things we are good at or enjoy. Helping a young person with autism to develop their hobbies and interests – perhaps supporting them to join a club – may be a really positive way to help them feel good about themselves and their abilities. Volunteering may also be an option. There are lots of opportunities out there to volunteer and for those young people who may need a bit more support, supported volunteering opportunities may be available in some places. Helping others can really help people to feel good about themselves. For young people with autism, this may be a great way to help them become less isolated and build on their strengths or develop new skills. See the Useful links section for ideas on how to find volunteering opportunities.

Activity

> What things does my child enjoy?
> What local groups or clubs exist that link to their interests?
> What volunteering opportunities might they enjoy?

Developing assertiveness skills

Helping a young person with autism to develop confidence and become assertive can help to make them more resilient and better able to navigate the complex social world we live in.

This can start in very simple ways by giving a young person responsibility in the home for particular tasks. As well as learning the positive feelings that come with contributing to family life, it will also help them to pick up the very important skill of doing things even when we'd rather not, in order to help others and 'chip in' to family life.

Helping a young person to balance activity and rest is also important in developing a sense of wellbeing. Having time alone is often important to people with autism, and scheduling time for a young person to be alone to pursue particular interests can also be key.

Working to help a young person to communicate what they want to do is an important first step in developing assertiveness skills. It can be effective to use a cue card or object to help a young person to remember to stop and think about what they want. Providing examples of assertive communication that allows them to look after their needs is also essential. These might include phrases like 'I don't agree with you', 'I need five minutes alone' or 'Please explain that again'. Being able to use assertive statements for communicating needs is essential, as they can be a way out of difficult situations, which if unchecked could lead to displaying inappropriate behaviour and therefore unpopularity. Teaching these appropriate ways to speak and communicate will help a young person to develop self-confidence and their sense of being in control. For children whose expressive language is limited, cue cards or traffic light cards can be used to help communicate when they are unhappy or want something to end.

Take the time to think about whom your child enjoys spending time with and what they might learn from them. It may be an older or younger sibling, or another child at school or at one of their activities. Young people build bonds with other adults in their lives too. Is there a youth worker, scout leader or a teacher they want to be like? Spending time together thinking about what they like about that person can help them to learn new positive behaviours. This kind of discussion may also be a good time to start to talk about people that they don't like and help to develop assertive strategies to cope with that person. Another important message is that we all feel different and out of place at times and many young people with autism talk about feeling different from their peers. As parents, helping them to understand that this is a normal part of growing up and that all young people feel like that at times may help them to accept themselves and will assist them in developing a positive sense of self-worth.

Activity

Develop a one-page profile or presentation with your child about themselves. They could use pictures, drawings, music, writing or any other way of expressing themselves.

Some questions to think about:

> What do I like to do?
> What things don't I like?
> What do other people say about me?
> How can other people help and support me?

These profiles or presentations could be shared with some of the people that work with your child. For example, the school, social workers and medical professionals. Perhaps everyone in the family could create their own profiles or presentations to share together?

(See Resource 6 on page 57 for a template for a short profile.)

There are many different ways to help you and your child remember the positive experiences and successes they have had. You can be creative in the ways you do this. You could try putting up pictures of happy events around your home and in your child's room to provide them with visual reminders of positive experiences. A diary may work in a similar way for an older child. Putting together a life-story book could also be helpful, fun and will give them lots of reminders of positive events to look at during more difficult times. Remember to provide reminders and rewards for your child's qualities as well as for good behaviour.

Managing anxiety

As we have seen, anxiety is a common difficulty for young people with autism. The world is a complicated place. It's unpredictable, loud and busy, with many unwritten rules. Finding strategies to reduce your child's anxiety and ways to assist them to manage it is important when helping them to develop a positive sense of wellbeing. Assertiveness and a sense of self-esteem are helpful tools in managing and reducing anxiety. In addition, positive communication and social skills will help to buffer the effects of anxiety on your child's wellbeing.

Communication

Communication is a many layered and complex process. Adapting how we communicate will help young people with autism to understand what is expected of them.

To ensure that communication is effective, the first step is to make sure you have your child's attention. There are some simple things we can do as adults to ensure that what we communicate is clear and understandable.

> Use your child's first name.

> Make sure you are in the same room and not calling to them from another place.

> If touching is not painful for your child, then a firm touch (without startling them) on the arm may help them to understand that you want their attention.

> Use a calm and clear voice.

> Get down to their level.

> Bear in mind that eye contact may be difficult for your child and that not looking at you may not mean they are not listening. In fact, asking them to look at you may reduce their ability to listen effectively.

> Give your child time to process what you have said and wait a few seconds before repeating anything. A six second rule is useful here to allow processing time without overloading your child with repetition as they try to process and formulate a response to what you have said.

> If you do need to repeat what you have said, try to use the same words.

> Use fewer words if processing is difficult. Particularly with older children, if you are using lots of words, make sure the key information is clearly structured within the sentence to avoid your child feeling frustrated and upset.

> Remember that your child may not know things unless you have told them explicitly. The difficulties inherent in autism mean that a good rule of thumb is to assume that if you haven't told your child something, they won't know it.

> Talk about things as they are happening as well as about things that are going to happen.

> If you are upset, wait until you feel calmer before explaining things to your child.

> Be careful about using phrases that are difficult to understand.

> Be precise in what you say. For example, 'Go and put your clothes in the drawer' rather than 'Go and tidy your room'.

> Use visual methods to support communication.

> For older children, use more 'grown-up' methods of visual communication such as mind maps and flow charts (some examples are given in the Resources and information section on page 40).

> Provide your child's day with structure. This does not mean doing the same thing each day but making sure that they know what is happening each day, what they need to do and that they know when activities start and end.

Links to information about resources to support communication are provided in the Useful links section.

Social skills

Social skills are the skills we need for life. Some of these are clear and can be taught as rules, for example showering each day and putting on deodorant and looking at people when you greet them. But social skills often relate to unwritten rules like when to be assertive or when to share. Helping children with autism to learn social skills gives them choices that will help them manage different situations in their daily life.

There are a number of references in the Useful links section to help young people learn social skills.

As well as social skills, it is important to teach conversation skills to young people with autism. There are numerous skills involved in having a conversation which include understanding what a conversation is and then specific factors that may need to be taught, such as:

> starting a conversation

> making eye contact

> respecting personal space

> taking turns

> keeping on topic

> talking about shared interests

> handling sensitive topics

> ending a conversation.

Social communication changes over time. New slang appears, cultures change and develop – and your child may need regular support with keeping their communication skills strong.

Chapter 3: daily life

Healthy living

As discussed in Chapter 2, a positive sense of self-esteem, positive activities and a strong social network are all essential elements in supporting our children's wellbeing. In addition, we need to support our children to live healthy lives. Diet and exercise are key parts of this.

Food is often something that causes difficulty for young people with autism. Textures, smells and colours can all make eating a wide and varied diet hard. We can encourage and support our children to try new things and be creative with food preparation to help them to have a balanced and healthy diet. Issues with foods and diet should always be treated carefully, and any concerns should be raised with a medical professional such as your GP in the first instance.

Encouraging young people to participate in preparing food – and, if possible, in growing food – are both positive steps towards encouraging your child to explore healthy eating. If you don't have much space, then simply growing lettuce and herbs on the kitchen windowsill or tomatoes or potatoes in a pot on the balcony or patio is enough to get them interested. If you have more space, then a raised bed for vegetables in the garden may be possible. Gardening brings with it a whole range of added benefits including light exercise and developing a tolerance to being messy, which can be difficult for some young people with autism. Learning to care for and nurture plants can also help to teach responsibility – they must be watered regularly, for example. There is little more satisfying and rewarding in life than eating something you have grown from the seed yourself.

If growing food is not an option then getting young people involved in cooking can help to decrease anxiety around food. By understanding what goes into different meals your child may become braver with regard to trying new things. Cooking as a way of contributing to and supporting the family has benefits too, and it's exciting to eat the cake made by your child when friends come to tea.

Your child may discover a real talent and even a future job or career through developing skills around food.

There are lots of resources on the web to help young people to learn about food, healthy eating, interesting recipes and ideas for growing food in a space of any size. Some links are included in the Useful links section.

Behaviour

Young people with autism often find things difficult, and sometimes this will mean that they behave in puzzling or challenging ways. As they get older and reach puberty, the way they behave may change, or become more challenging. Many teenagers, including those without autism, become moody and 'difficult' with the onset of puberty and the increase in hormones and other changes occurring in their bodies. This is a normal part of growing up, but it can still be a difficult time for parents and young people alike. As Dean Beadle points out in his foreword, it is a complex time. Changes in the body, sleep issues, and the endless pressures that any young person faces to 'fit in' and navigate the increasingly multifaceted social relationships they encounter as they grow up, can all have an effect.

Helping your child to understand and manage their own behaviour is an essential part of our role as parents in helping them to navigate their journey to adulthood.

It can be helpful to think about behaviour as an iceberg. The behaviour itself is the part that is visible above the waterline, but the reasons for that behaviour are hidden beneath the water. Finding out what lies beneath the waterline is the key to helping your child to manage and understand their behaviour and to change it if they want to.

Behaviours that seem puzzling to those of us without autism are not always bad. Obviously, if a young person with autism is harming themselves or others we need to take action to help them redirect or stop the behaviour, and if necessary seek professional advice and support. But some behaviour that may appear odd or strange could be very successful ways of coping with overwhelming feelings or experiences.

In these instances, we need to understand if the behaviour is causing your child any distress or anxiety.

One example is hand-flapping. While in itself not a harmful behaviour, your child may feel embarrassed or uncomfortable when they do this in front of their classmates or friends. In this case, working with your child to understand what function the behaviour serves is important. Perhaps the reason for the hand-flapping is a way of reducing a build-up of anxiety. Once you understand the function of a behaviour, you can help your child to find different ways of managing their anxiety. In this example, you could provide some ideas for hand-flapping in private, such as asking to leave the classroom and go to a quiet room to hand-flap for a minute without being observed by classmates. Another solution might be doing an activity that helps your child to shake the anxiety away. Taking a dance or movement class could help them to reduce the instances of the behaviour they find embarrassing by giving a new and socially appropriate outlet.

Other strategies for reducing the anxiety in this instance might include agreeing with the school that your child doesn't need to take that particular class. This is not always possible but it is worth discussing it with the school.

Ask the questions:

> Could your child take a different option at that time?

> Could the teacher give you the lesson plans for the term so that your child knows what will happen in that lesson before he or she goes to class?

> Could the teacher incorporate more opportunities to move around into the lesson, or send the young person on an errand if they notice they are getting anxious?

> Could your child and the teacher agree a system whereby the young person is able to communicate discreetly that they are feeling anxious and need some additional support?

Another change that may help is agreeing with your child that they can have 45 minutes of 'alone time' once they come home from school before they will need to do anything else.

Activity

You can do this alone or with your child. Think about one specific behaviour that is causing your child distress.

Answer the following questions:

1. What is the behaviour?
2. Is it really a problem?
3. Is this the right time to tackle it?
4. Why does your child behave like this? Observe the behaviour, gather clues as to what causes it, think about where it happens and what triggers it.
5. What happens as a result of the behaviour?
6. How can we make the situation better?

    > Do we need to change the situation?
    > Do we need to change the way we communicate?
    > Would rewards be helpful?
    > What alternative behaviour do we want to see?
    > Do we need to teach this?

There may be various reasons for each of the behaviours and there are also many possible solutions. As with everything, creativity is the key[3], and there are lots of resources out there to help you to help your child. Some of these are listed in the Useful links section.

School

School can be a tricky place for any young person. For a young person with autism it can be incredibly difficult. The social nuances of the school environment are complex for any teenager to navigate, and can be perplexing to a young person with autism.

3. Hattersley, C. (2013). *Autism: understanding behaviour.* London: The National Autistic Society

Young people with autism may be more vulnerable to bullying than their peers and because of their difficulties, they may also be unable to communicate this to you. The Department for Education defines bullying as being:

> deliberately hurtful

> repeated over a period of time

> difficult for victims to defend themselves against.

Bullying falls into three main categories:

> physical – including hitting, kicking, and taking belongings

> verbal – name-calling, insulting or making offensive remarks, for example

> indirect – spreading nasty stories about someone, exclusion from social groups, being made the subject of malicious rumours or sending malicious emails or text messages on mobile phones, for example.[4]

As well as bullying at school, technology such as the internet and mobile phones allow bullies to act in different ways and outside school hours. Children with special educational needs are more likely to be bullied than their peers.[5]

Children with autism communicate differently. They may have difficulty reading facial expressions and understanding the intentions of other people. This means they are especially vulnerable to being bullied. The desire to make friends can also lead to children with autism following instructions from others to try to fit in with their peer group, including doing things that may hurt them or get them in trouble with school staff.

Children with autism can also become the bully themselves, perhaps becoming aggressive when a game is not played in the way they want or getting frustrated at being left out and trying to get other children to be friends with them.

4. Department for Education (2002). *Bullying: don't suffer in silence.* London: Department for Education

5. Chatzitheochari, S et al (2014). *Bullying victimisation among disabled children and young people: Evidence from two British longitudinal studies.* London: The Institute of Education

It is not easy for parents to know if their children are being bullied as your child may not know they are being bullied. The NSPCC gives some useful suggestions to help you tell whether or not your child is being bullied.

> Have their belongings been taken or damaged?
> Are they over-tired and hungry from not eating lunch (if their dinner money or lunch has been taken)?
> Are they afraid to go to school? Are they mysteriously 'ill' each morning, or skip school?
> Have they shown a drop in performance at school?
> Do they ask for, or steal, money (to pay)?
> Are they afraid of travelling on the school bus or on their own to school?
> Are they nervous or distressed, or have they lost confidence?
> Have they stopped eating or sleeping?
> Have they begun to bully others?
> Have they refused to say what's wrong or become withdrawn?
> Are they physically injured? [6]

A child with autism may also show sudden changes in behaviour which may be linked to bullying at school. This could include increased anxiety and outbursts at home. They may also mimic the actions of bullies at school by bullying siblings at home.

If you are concerned about your child, in the first instance you can try to talk to them about it, or contact the school to raise your concerns. Schools take bullying very seriously and should move to tackle any problems immediately.

There are links to further support and information on this subject in the Useful links section.

---

6. NSPCC (2014). *Bullying*. www.nspcc.org.uk/help-and-advice/worried-about-a-child/online-advice/bullying/bullying-a_wda87098.html (Accessed: 30 August 2014).

Transitions and planning for the future

Preparing to leave school is one of the most challenging and exciting times for any young person. For a young person with autism, it can be fraught with difficulties and supporting your child to navigate this transition is another very important part of helping them to prepare positively for adult life.

Many young people with autism go on to study in further or higher education. The support provided in different colleges and universities can vary, so careful preparation is needed to make sure your child has a positive experience. The first step for parents is to find out about the choices available and the processes involved in getting to the desired outcome. Legal frameworks outlining the support that disabled young people are entitled to change over time. There are also differences in different countries. However, there are lots of organisations that can help you with finding the most up-to-date information and guidance. Some links are listed in the Useful links section.

For young people with autism, transition can be a difficult time. Choices are many and varied. Do they opt for college, university, employment, apprenticeships, volunteering or something else? Making sure that young people have the skills to manage the next stage of their lives is an essential part of growing up. For example, going to university away from home may mean that a young person needs to be able to cook, clean and use a washing machine alongside the academic requirements for whatever course they want to study. Social skills are also essential when integrating into a new environment. For this reason, the sooner you can start planning with your teenage son or daughter about their next steps, the better. It will give them more time to develop and practise the required skills to make it a success.

If independent living is not an option for your child, they may still be able to study at university level, either by finding a local university where they can continue to live at home or by finding online, distance and evening courses that will help them to reach their desired goals.

Some local further education (FE) colleges also offer foundation degrees in a number of subjects which may be an option. If your child chooses employment or volunteering as their next step, you will need to think about what skills they will need to develop to make this possible.

Activity

Spend some time with your son or daughter thinking about what they want to do next in their life, when school finishes.

Think about their interests, their skills and experience. In the early stages, this can be on a very general level and over time these discussions and ideas will solidify into some tangible options. This is not a one-time discussion.

You can use a range of resources to help you. Autobiographies of people with autism, videos and other resources might help to spark ideas and help your child see what might be possible.

Frame the discussions carefully to try and avoid raising anxiety levels for your child about an unknown future that they may struggle to visualise. You could use the short profile template on page 57 to think about what your child likes, is good at and what they may need to help them achieve their desired goals.

Technology

Using technology is a popular activity among many young people with autism for learning, to support communication, to help with remembering schedules, for social networking and for play. The uses are endless and lots of new technologies and apps are being developed all the time.

Technology can be really helpful to children and young people with autism. For example, it can:

> help them to learn and practise new skills

> be intrinsically motivating

> help them to make their own choices about what they learn and how they play

> help them engage others both online through social media and offline by talking about what they have done

> allow them to have regular, discreet and socially acceptable access to things that help them to manage their anxiety, such as a particular piece of music, or a game.

Links to information on the use of technology are included in the Useful links section.

Despite having many positives, there are also risks related to using technology. It is important to allow your child to engage in technology as this is a normal part of growing up, but as parents we can also teach our children to use online communities and social networks safely and be on the alert for cyber bullying and other possible threats. Use technology as one of many different approaches when supporting your child to develop and learn.

Chapter 4: relationships

In this section, we will be exploring the issues around relationships, sex and puberty. These are often difficult subjects and as parents you will need to think carefully about what areas you will discuss with your child and the way you will discuss them. It is important that you choose what you are comfortable with, and don't feel that you have to cover everything that is outlined here. Families all have different ways of dealing with this area. As a parent, your beliefs and values will play an important part in helping you to decide how to address the subject.

The resources in this section are suggestions that others have used to support young people with autism to understand this complex and sometimes confusing area. Make sure you adapt these to support your child's understanding and make sure they understand and are not worried or anxious.

Puberty and sexuality

People with autism have the same drives and desires as everybody else, but because sexuality involves social communication and interaction, they may express their needs in a different way. This complexity means they are likely to need more detailed information and education about puberty, sexuality and relationships than other young people.

All children and young people will get a certain amount of education on these subjects at school. At primary school, this is likely to consist of naming parts of the body and learning information about changes to the body during puberty. In secondary school, this will include the biology of human reproduction and other elements that may also be taught as part of Personal, Social, Health and Economic Education (PSHEE) or its equivalent.

Activity

Before you begin to think about this issue, make sure you are clear in your mind on what you want to teach your child. You can do this individually or with your partner.

Think about the following questions:

> What are my beliefs and values about sex and sexuality?

> What do I want my child to understand about this area?

> How do I feel about talking about these things?

> What resources might I need to support me to communicate effectively on this subject? See the Useful resources section for links and ideas.

> What is my child's level of understanding?

> What support do I need to prepare for as a result of this discussion?

There are a few things you can do to help your child understand puberty and sexuality.

> Make sure they know they can talk to you about anything.

> Make sure they understand that questions and concerns are normal and perfectly natural.

> Start providing information early.

> Provide information that is clear and easy to follow.

> Give your child information in small sections that builds up over time.

> Provide opportunities to practise developing relationships safely.

> Talk to the school about what they will be teaching and when so you can prepare your child beforehand and follow up afterwards.

Preparing your child for adult life

The goal for our child's teenage years is to prepare them for their adult life. Among many other skills, this also includes preparing them to enjoy sexual activity, whether that's alone, with another person or both. It also includes helping them to understand how to stay safe and to deal with unwanted attention or abuse. To do this, we need to help them to become sexually confident. The following checklist[7] outlines some key skills that you can teach your child with this goal in mind.

Sexual confidence and safety checklist

Does your child:

> understand what sexual behaviour is
> have the skills to have sex and enjoy sexual activity
> understand pregnancy and contraception
> understand what is legally acceptable and what is not
> have an understanding of the core values of relationships
> know about sexually transmitted diseases and how to practise safe sex
> know where and when to do sexual activities
> understand how to report unwanted attention
> know the difference between fact and fantasy
> have an understanding of personal safety?

The key skills to develop during puberty are:

> washing regularly including key parts of the body
> wearing deodorant
> learning how to shave particular areas of the body
> wearing supportive underwear (eg a bra for a girl)
> skin care and spot treatments

7. Nichols, S., Moravick, G. M. and Tetenbaum, S. P. (2009). *Girls growing up on the autism spectrum: what parents and professionals should know about the pre-teen and teenage years.* London: Jessica Kingsley Publishers

> grooming and teeth brushing

> having an understanding of sanitary care products (girls)

> having an understanding of erections and wet dreams (boys)

> having an understanding of masturbation

> the difference between public and private behaviours.

Sex and the law

The age of consent for sex in the UK is 16 for both boys and girls. Young people with learning disabilities can give consent at age 16 if the individual can 'agree by choice and has freedom and capacity to make that choice.'[8] If two people who both cannot give consent have sex they will not be prosecuted – if they both have severe learning disabilities, for example. However if anyone else has sex with someone who cannot give consent they will be prosecuted under the Sexual Offences Act 2003.

People with learning disabilities can also get married at 16 with parental consent and at 18 without, just the same as everyone else. If there is concern about your child's ability to consent to marriage, then the correct official has to be notified (the registrar or religious official, for example). Divorce law is also the same for people with learning difficulties.

The *Sexual Offences Act 2003* also includes provision for a number of new offences against people with a mental disorder, which is defined as including those with a 'disability of the mind'. This will often include those with autism. It is illegal for a care worker to engage in sexual activity with someone who has a mental disorder. This includes cases where a worker tells the person that the sexual act was just providing 'personal care'. It is also an offence to engage anyone with a mental disorder in sexual activity by inducement, threat or deception. This could include someone with a disability being told that they will get into trouble or be laughed at unless they have sex with the perpetrator. It could also include someone being bribed to have sex or being misled – for example, being told they should because 'this is what friends do for each other'.

8. HM Government (2003). *Sexual Offences Act 2003.* www.legislation.gov.uk/ukpga/2003/42/contents (Accessed 30 August 2014)

Puberty

Puberty is the term we use to describe the changes a person's body goes through as it develops and matures. It can begin at any time from age 8 to 15 years and finishes around 18 years of age.

Hygiene

Teaching our children appropriate hygiene routines becomes increasingly important as puberty progresses. Changes to the body will affect how frequently they will need to wash and what products they will need to use. Sensory sensitivities can make this especially difficult for young people with autism. The scent of shampoo, the feel of a foaming facial wash, the sound of a spray deodorant or the feel of a particular sanitary product could all have an impact and make this transition more complicated for young people with autism. However a lot of products are now available to choose from, so a little patience in finding the right ones will help your child to manage these new changes.

Public and private

Understanding the difference between public and private is essential as your child moves into adulthood. The things your child needs to be able to understand during puberty and young adulthood are:

> private places

> private parts

> who you can touch

> who can touch you

> that you can decide who touches your body

> which people can kiss you, hug you and shake your hand

> good touch and bad touch

> reporting bad touch

> public and private behaviours

> being able to say 'no'

> where the dangers are.

These topics are some of the trickiest that parents have to tackle with their children as they grow up. There are some links to help you to do this in a positive way with your child in the Useful links section.

A message to parents

As parents, we are the most important resource that our children have. We are their allies, a source of information and the people that will help them develop a strong sense of self-esteem. Therefore, it's really important to look after yourself as well as your child.

Take time out for yourself when you can. This is vital to support your wellbeing as well as your child's. It's not being selfish, it's about ensuring you have the internal resources you need to support your child as well as you can. If you are tired or irritable it will be harder for you to stay calm and avoid losing your temper – and our children can pick up on our moods.

The difficulties your child may face stem from the fact that they have fewer skills to manage their daily life and are nothing to do with your parenting ability. As parents we can, of course, make things better or worse for our children. But you could be the best parent in the world and your child could still face difficulties. This is because the world we live in is not particularly autism friendly.

There is no such thing as the perfect parent. We all make mistakes, but what matters is the long-term message we give to our children – that you love them and think they are amazing!

There will be days when things go wrong and others when it's hard to find the energy to put them right. In reality, most parents will shout at their children at some point. The aim is to be good enough and to avoid wasting time on feeling guilty or worrying about what is in the past when time and energy can be better invested in helping your child now.

As someone very wise once said to me when talking about her child – you just have to do your best, apologise when you get it wrong and, most importantly, just make sure they know that you love them.

Resources and information
for you and your child

You can photocopy the resources and the information in this section,
or use them as guidance when creating your own. You and your child
can do the activities together, or your child could do them on their own, or
with the help of a sibling or friend.

Resource 1: my body

Your child can do this by themselves, with you, a sibling or a friend.

Human beings are complex with lots of different parts that help us to live and be healthy.

1. Draw an outline of a person in the space below.
2. Draw in the parts of the body – liver, kidneys, heart, lungs, brain and stomach.
3. Draw in any other parts of the body that you want to.

Resource 2: my amazing brain

Your child can do this by themselves, with you, a sibling or a friend.

1. Read the text below.

My brain is amazing! It can do thousands of things at the same time. Different parts of the brain have different jobs to do:

> part of my brain tells me when I am hungry or thirsty
> part of my brain tells me when it is time to sleep
> part of my brain tells me when it is time to go to the toilet
> part of my brain helps me to stand up and balance
> part of my brain helps me to walk and run
> part of my brain helps me to write
> part of my brain helps me to draw
> part of my brain helps me to listen
> part of my brain helps me to speak
> part of my brain helps me to remember things.

There are different parts of my brain that help me to stay in control when I am angry or upset.

There are different parts of my brain which help me to understand what other people are feeling.

My brain helps me to think about things.

My brain helps me to feel different things like being happy, sad, angry or excited.

Everybody's brain makes them think a little bit differently.

My brain makes me think differently from other people.

There are many different types of thinking.

All the ways of thinking are important.

Everybody's brain makes them good at some things.

Everybody's brain makes them not very good at other things.

Different people are good at different things:

> some people are good at sports
> some people are good at talking
> some people are good at listening
> some people are good at maths
> some people are good at making things
> some people are good at helping other people
> some people are good at being happy and smiling
> some people are good at remembering things
> some people are good at computer games
> some people are good at music
> some people are good at other things.

The most important things to be good at are:

> being friendly to other people
> being happy
> being kind to yourself.

2. **Draw an outline of your head in the box opposite.**

3. **Inside the picture of your head, draw a picture of your brain – you can copy from a book or get pictures from the internet to help you.**

4. **Find out what the different areas of the brain do and label them on the drawing.**

5. **On the next page, write down some of the things your brain makes you good at.**

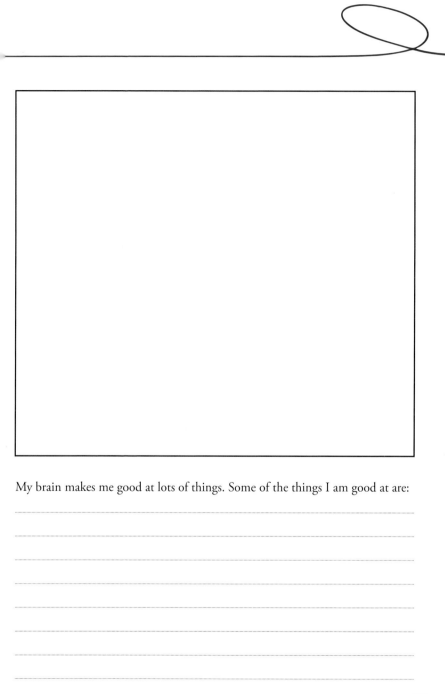

My brain makes me good at lots of things. Some of the things I am good at are:

Resource 3: about me

You might like to get everyone in your family to complete this resource and compare notes.

Every child in the world is different. They have different hair colour, eye colour and are good at different things.

Draw a picture of yourself in the space below. If you don't want to draw a picture you could stick in a photograph or ask someone else to draw a picture of you.

My name is

....

I am................................years old.

I am good at

....

....

....

....

....

....

....

My favourite things are

....

....

....

....

....

....

....

Resource 4: finding out about other people

You can adapt this to incorporate the important people in your child's life. Your child could do this activity by interviewing people to find out about them.

Mum likes

Dad likes

My sister/brother likes

Mum is good at

Dad is good at

....

....

....

....

My sister/brother is good at

....

....

....

....

Mum finds it difficult

....

....

....

....

Dad finds it difficult

....

....

....

....

My sister/brother finds it difficult

....

....

....

Resource 5: what is autism?

Use this as a guide and adapt it for your child.

Autism can be called different things.

People with autism have a brain that works differently to most other people.

It means that they think differently to most other people.

Having autism means it can take practice to make friends.

About 1 in 100 people have autism.

Many people have a brain that makes it easier to make friends but people with autism can still learn how to make friends.

Some people with autism find it hard to make friends easily.

Which of these things apply to you?

☐ I find making friends difficult

☐ I like things being different

☐ I like going to the cinema

☐ I like pizza

☐ I like it when things change

☐ I like playing on the computer

☐ I like talking to other children at school

☐ I like surprises

☐ I like flapping my hands sometimes

☐ I like running

☐ I like it when things are the same

☐ I like having time alone

☐ I like taking things apart to see how they work

☐ I like my brother/sister

☐ I like loud noises

☐ I like being in my room

☐ I like all the children in my class

☐ I like some of the children in my class

☐ I like my teacher

☐ I like birthday parties

☐ I like chocolate

☐ I like doing sport at school

Other things I like are

_____

_____

_____

_____

_____

_____

_____

_____

_____

Information about being me

Use this as a guide and adapt it for your child, adding more examples if needed.

I am a very important and precious person to my parents and my family.

I am good at doing lots of things.

Mum, dad and my teachers can help me with things I find difficult.

The name for how I think is called 'autism'.

Other people, including some famous people, have a brain like mine.

People cannot see that I have autism because it is inside my brain.

I am loved by lots of people.

I can make other people happy by being a friendly person.

People have different ways of thinking.

Some people are logical thinkers, they are clever at some things, but get stuck on other things.

They think in a logical way.

Other people are not as logical and make decisions based on their emotions. They can be clever at some things too and also get stuck on some things too.

The world needs people who think in different ways.

I am good at:

> reading

> numbers

> drawing

> using computers

> remembering things

> looking after the cat.

There are some things I find difficult:

> changes

> looking at people's faces

> knowing how I feel

> being in a large group.

Everyone has things that they are good at and things they find difficult:

> finding things difficult does not stop me being a great person

> people who find things difficult can still do amazing things

> people who are disabled can still do great things

> people who cannot see can still do great things

> people who cannot hear can still do great things

> people who cannot walk can still do great things

> people who cannot make friends very easily can still do great things

> everyone finds some things difficult

> everyone can still do amazing things.

What is a disability?

A disability is what you call it when someone finds it very difficult or impossible to do certain things.

Some people are deaf.

Being deaf is a disability.

If someone is deaf they cannot hear very well or at all.

Some people are blind.

Being blind is a disability.

If someone is blind they cannot see very well or at all.

Some people are physically disabled.

Being physically disabled is a disability.

Some people who are physically disabled use a wheelchair or other support to move around because they can't walk very well or not at all.

Many people think autism is a disability.

This is because if you have autism then making friends and understanding other people is often difficult.

There are lots of people with disabilities in the world.

They find some things difficult and some things easy, just like everyone else.

Information about having autism

Use this as a guide and adapt it for your child, adding more examples if needed.

There are about 1 in 100 people with autism in the UK.

That's about 800,000 people.

Everyone, with or without autism, should be treated with kindness and care.

Having autism does not make you better than anyone else.

Having autism does not make you worse than anyone else.

Having autism makes you think a bit differently to most other people. This can make you feel a bit different to everyone else.

People with autism do lots of things the same as anyone else.

> You do most things the same as everyone else.

> You have things you like the same as everyone else.

> You have things you don't like the same as everyone else.

> You have things that make you happy the same as everyone else.

> You have things that make you angry the same as everyone else.

> You walk and run the same as everyone else.

> You need to eat, drink and use the toilet the same as everyone else.

People with autism are amazing.

Having autism can make you amazing at doing some things.

> There are some people with autism who are amazing at being kind and friendly.

> There are some people with autism who are amazing at thinking about things no one else has ever thought about before.

> There are some people with autism who are amazing artists.

> There are some people with autism who are amazing actors.

> There are some people with autism who are amazing inventors.

> There are some people with autism who are amazing singers.

> There are some people with autism who are amazing designers.

All people with autism are amazing.

All people without autism are amazing too.

No one knows exactly why people have autism, and it is nobody's fault that you have autism.

It does not mean there is something wrong with you; you were just born with autism. It is not a disease, illness or medical problem and it will not harm you, it is just about how your brain works, a different way of thinking.

Other people in your family may have autism or they may not. You cannot give it to other people. People with autism are amazing and can do lots of great things.

Having autism can make life harder sometimes. You will have things that you try that you find difficult and you will learn different ways to be happy and get along with people.

If you have questions you want answered about having autism you can ask your mum or dad to answer them or look online at **www.autism.org.uk**.

If you want to talk to someone else about having autism you can tell your mum or dad so they can help you find someone to talk to.

Sometimes you might wish that you did not have autism. You may feel angry, frustrated, upset or sad. It's okay to feel like this sometimes.

Talk to your mum or dad, or someone else that you trust as they might be able to help you to feel better.

Resource 6: short profile

Your child can do this by themselves, with you, a sibling or a friend. You might also like to do this with all members of your family. You can also change and adapt the sections to suit your child's needs. A link to more information on short profiles (also called one-page profiles) is given in the Useful links section.

Short profile for:

My picture (this can be a photo or a drawing)

Things I like

Things I don't like

Things people say about me

Ways other people can support me

Resource 7: mind-map

There are lots of resources available for making visual supports for children and young people. For teenagers, it may be appropriate to use technology to support communication rather than pictures, or you could use more 'grown up' resources that adults also use such as mind mapping or flow charts to think about communication or any other issues.

This is an example of a mind map for saying hello to different people.

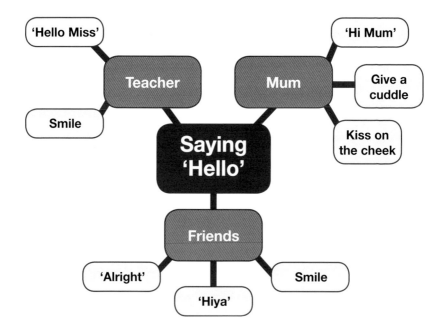

This is an example flow chart for talking about Dr Who.

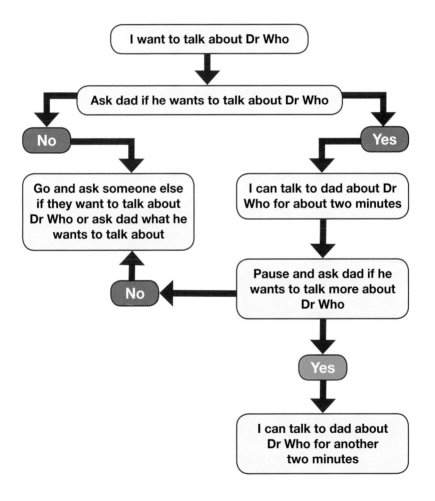

Resource 8: letter template

This can be adapted to incorporate the unique preferences of your child.

This is a template for a letter to school friends and classmates about having autism.

My name is_____

I want to tell you about autism.

You may have noticed that I sometimes do things differently to most other people.

For example:

> I don't usually join in games in the playground

> I always sit on the end of a row near the door in class and assembly

> there are some things I am not very good at talking about

> I love to talk about_____ and sometimes I don't know when to stop

> sometimes I get annoyed or upset and have to leave the classroom

> I don't always understand jokes

> I can't always work out what other people are feeling

> sometimes I say things that are rude or inappropriate without realising it

> I forget to say 'hello' back to people that say 'hello' to me

> sometimes it might seem like I am in my own world

> sometimes I repeat what someone else has just said

> sometimes I talk under my breath instead of thinking of things in my head

> sometimes I appear to be ignoring other people.

The reason I do these things is because I have autism.

Autism is the name given by doctors to people that find making friends and understanding other people difficult.

Having autism means that I don't always understand what I am supposed to do or how to act with other people.

Having autism makes life difficult for me because I do want to get along with people and be friendly with everyone.

Autism is not a disease or illness and it's not catching.

You can help me in lots of ways.

> When you say hello and I ignore you, you can remind me that it is polite to say hello back to someone.

> In the playground if I am standing on my own, you can come and talk to me, I may sometimes want to be alone, but you can ask me if I want to talk.

> You can save a seat at the end of a row for me in assembly.

> You can help me understand if you are happy, sad or angry by telling me that is how you feel.

> If I talk too much about_____ you can tell me that I need to talk about something else for a while, or that I need to listen to you for a while.

If you have any questions about autism you can ask_____ (name of teacher or other person at school who is prepared to help with this).

Thank you.

Resource 9: private body parts and private places

This should be adapted for your child's age and level of understanding. It is a guide for you to use and adapt according to your family's values and beliefs.

Private can mean many different things.

What are private parts?
Private parts on boys and men are the penis, testicles and bottom.
Private parts on girls and women are the vagina, inner thighs, breasts and bottom.

What are private places?
Private places are places where it is okay to touch your own private parts or the private parts of your boyfriend or girlfriend.
Private places are your bedroom or bathroom at home.

Talking about private things
Some things are private, and some private things are to do with your body.

There are some private things to do with your body, these are:

> your private parts

> periods

> masturbating

> doing a poo.

I can talk to some people about these private things, they are:

> my mum and dad

> my auntie

> my teacher

> the doctor or nurse at my surgery.

Who can touch my private parts?

Your girlfriend or boyfriend might touch your private parts.

Your doctor or a nurse might touch your private parts if you are feeling unwell in those places.

It is not okay for anyone else to touch your private parts.

It is not okay for anyone else to touch your clothes in places they cover your private parts.

It is not okay for anyone to touch your thighs near your private parts.

If someone does touch you in those places you should say 'NO' in a loud voice and tell a trusted adult as soon as possible.

Underwear

For girls underwear is knickers and bra.
For boys underwear is underpants or boxer shorts.

Naked is what you call it when you take all your clothes off
There are other words for naked – being nude, for example.

In some places it is okay to be in your underwear or naked.
These are private places.

Your private places are:

> in your bedroom if the door is shut
> the toilet if the door is shut and locked
> the bathroom if the door is shut and locked
> the swimming pool changing room
> the school changing room.

Sometimes we see other people's underwear.

For women this might be part of a bra strap or part of their knickers.

For men this might be part of their underpants if they like to wear their trousers a little bit lower than their underpants.

This is okay and is normal. You should not tell the person that you can see part of their underwear.

You might also see other young people at school or at a sports club in their underwear or naked when you are changing for PE, swimming, gymnastics, football, dance class, or wearing costumes in a play. This is okay and normal.

Activity

Think about when and where it is okay to take off your underwear on the chart below.

Okay to take off underwear?			
Inside	**Yes/No**	**Outside**	**Yes/No**
Lounge		Park	
Bathroom		Swimming pool	
Toilet		Swimming pool changing room	
Bedroom		Car park	
Mum and Dad's bedroom		Public toilet urinal	
Brother's bedroom		Public toilet cubicle	
Sister's bedroom		Friend's house toilet	
Garden		Doctors waiting room	
Garage		Hospital cubicle	
When wearing a bathrobe		Doctors consulting room	
		On the beach	

Information about puberty

Puberty is the name given to the changes that happen in your body as you grow up.

It can start anytime between 8 and 15 years but typically it does not start until someone is around ten years old or older. During puberty your body changes and develops and you become stronger and able to do new things. Puberty ends when you are about 17 or 18 years old. It doesn't matter what age you start or finish puberty; everyone's body works a little bit differently.

Puberty is part of growing up. It is part of becoming an adult. It means you will be listened to more and have more freedom to decide what you want. During puberty your body changes. Below are some of the changes that occur during puberty:

Puberty in boys	Puberty in girls
May grow and get taller	May grow and get taller
Voice gets deeper	Breasts may grow
May start growing hair on your face, underarms, legs, pubic area and chest	May grow hair on your legs, underarms and pubic area
Shoulders get broader	Hips may get wider
May get spots	May get spots
Penis grows a bit larger	Period may start
Testicles get bigger	

Puberty is caused by your brain and body making more hormones. You cannot see hormones as they move around inside your body making you stronger and more grown up. Boys make hormones called testosterone and girls make hormones called oestrogen and progesterone.

During puberty you may experience more up and down feelings than before. This means you may feel very happy and at other times you might feel really sad or angry. These are sometimes called 'mood swings'. Once you are an adult you may have fewer 'mood swings' because the hormones in your body settle down again.

During puberty your body and brain get even better. They are an important part of how you become stronger and more intelligent. You will learn lots of new skills and your body develops and grows. You do not lose control in puberty, and no one can make you do anything you don't want to. Puberty is a natural part of life and happens to everyone. Remember, you are still you – whatever age you are.

In law you become an adult at 18 and when you finish puberty and are 18 you will be an adult. Some people are frightened of puberty because they don't want to be an adult. Being an adult means you can do more things than before. When you are an adult you usually have more control to choose what you do each day.

What might happen during puberty?

During puberty your body may grow	Some young people grow a lot taller, others stay pretty much the same height as they were. This is okay. Everyone grows at different speeds. Being tall or shorter doesn't matter, what is important is what kind of person you can be. Being a kind and friendly person is the most important thing.
During puberty you sweat more	Part of growing up is sweating more. Sweat is water mixed with salts, proteins and fatty acids. Unless you wash more often, the sweat reacts with the air and bacteria feed on the skin. This causes you to smell unpleasant to other people. If you do not wash regularly during puberty, you will develop body odour (BO) which smells unpleasant. This might mean other people don't want to be around you.

During puberty you might find you enjoy spending more time in your room	This is okay. It is important that you have time on your own to relax and do things you enjoy doing on your own. During puberty some young people like to play music in their room, play computer games, read books or magazines and watch TV.
During puberty you might find you have strong feelings about things	During puberty there are more hormones going round your body, these hormones might make you have strong feelings. Not everyone has strong feelings during puberty but a lot of young people do. Sometimes you might feel really happy or very sad, a lot of the time you might feel just alright. Having strong feelings is a normal part of life when your body is getting stronger and your brain is becoming more intelligent. If you want to talk to someone about your feelings ask your parents or a teacher if they can help.
During puberty your skin changes	During puberty your skin can feel more oily. This is because the glands under your skin (called sebaceous glands) produce more of an oily substance called sebum. This is just a normal part of growing up and becoming a more mature person.
During puberty you may get spots	Most people get some spots on their face. Some people do not. Spots can also be called other things, like pimples, acne or white heads. Some people get a lot of spots and need a special medication to help them with this. You should wash your face with a mild soap and warm water every day to help reduce spots. You may also get spots in other places like your neck or back. If you do get lots of spots it can make you feel a bit unhappy. If that happens, talk to your parents or a teacher if you want to. They may be able to help.

Checklist for parents: puberty skills

Key skills to teach your child during puberty:

- [ ] washing regularly
- [ ] washing key parts of the body
- [ ] wearing deodorant
- [ ] learning how to shave underarms and legs (for girls)
- [ ] shaving the face (for boys)
- [ ] wearing a bra (for girls)
- [ ] skin care for spots
- [ ] grooming
- [ ] teeth brushing
- [ ] tampons, towels and sanitary care (for girls)
- [ ] understanding about erections (for boys)
- [ ] understanding wet dreams (for boys)
- [ ] understanding about masturbation
- [ ] understanding the difference between public and private.

Useful links

Chapter 1: what is autism?

The National Autistic Society
The NAS website has lots of useful resources to help you understand and explain a diagnosis to your child.
www.autism.org.uk

You can also get advice and support from the helpline.
Call: **0808 800 4104**
Email: **autismhelpline@nas.org.uk**
Website: **www.autism.org.uk/helpline**

BBC, CBBC Programmes, Newsround (2012). *My autism and me*
www.bbc.co.uk/newsround/15655232
A 15-minute film about what it is like to have autism.

The National Autistic Society (2014). *Real-life stories*
www.autism.org.uk/living-with-autism/real-life-stories
Real-life stories about living with autism.

Chapter 2: wellbeing

Volunteering
Community Service Volunteers (CSV)
This charity can help you find links to volunteering opportunities.
Call: **020 7278 6601**
Email: **information@csv.org.uk**
Website: **www.csv.org.uk**

Profile information
Helen Sanderson Associates (2014) *One-page profiles*
www.helensandersonassociates.co.uk/reading-room/how/person-centred-thinking/one-page-profiles

Information on different visual supports
The National Autistic Society (2014). *Visual supports*
www.autism.org.uk/visualsupports

Social skills information
The National Autistic Society (2014). *Social skills for adolescents and adults*
www.autism.org.uk/socialskills

Social stories information
The Gray Centre (2014). *Social Stories*
www.thegraycenter.org/social-stories

Socialeyes information
The National Autistic Society (2014). *Socialeyes facilitator training*
www.autism.org.uk/socialeyes

Chapter 3: daily life

Information on understanding dietary issues in autism
The National Autistic Society (2014). *Dietary management for children and adolescents*
www.autism.org.uk/dietarymanagement

Information on sensory issues in autism
The National Autistic Society (2014). *The sensory world of autism*
www.autism.org.uk/sensory

Healthy eating
NHS Choices (2014). *Healthy Eating*
www.nhs.uk/livewell/healthy-eating/Pages/Healthyeating.aspx
Young Minds (2014). *Eat well, feel better.*
bit.ly/1rk4MYU

Gardening for people with special needs

RHS SEN Schools Project 2009-2010 (2010).
Growing Together: Gardening with Children and Young People with Special Educational Needs.
apps.rhs.org.uk/schoolgardening/uploads/documents/sen_report2009-10_final_1049.pdf

Understanding behaviour

The National Autistic Society (2014). *Understanding behaviour*
www.autism.org.uk/living-with-autism/understanding-behaviour

Information on education

The National Autistic Society (2014). *Education and transition*
www.autism.org.uk/living-with-autism/education-and-transition

Information for young people about bullying

The National Autistic Society (2014). *Bullying: a guide for young people*
www.autism.org.uk/living-with-autism/education-and-transition/bullying-guide-for-young-people

Information for parents about bullying

The National Autistic Society (2014). *Bullying: a guide for parents*
www.autism.org.uk/bullying

Transition to adulthood

The National Autistic Society (2014). *Education and transition*
www.autism.org.uk/education

Information about using technology for young people with autism

The National Autistic Society (2014). *Using technology: guidance for parents*
www.autism.org.uk/technology

Online safety

NSPCC (2014). *Online safety*
www.nspcc.org.uk/preventing-abuse/keeping-children-safe/online-safety

Online safety
Department for Education and Childnet (2013). *Cyberbullying and children and young people with SEN and disabilities: guidance for teachers and other professionals* **www.anti-bullyingalliance.org.uk/media/7441/cyberbullying-and-send-module-final.pdf**

Childnet (2014). *Star SEN toolkit* **www.childnet.com/resources/star-toolkit**

Chapter 4: relationships

An image vocabulary for children about feelings, rights and safety, personal care and sexuality
NSPCC (2014). *How it is: an image vocabulary for children about feelings, rights and safety, personal care and sexuality* **www.nspcc.org.uk/preventing-abuse/research-and-resources/how-it-is**

Puberty, the body and sex education
BBC (2014). *Science: human body & mind* **www.bbc.co.uk/science/humanbody/body/index.shtml?lifecycle**

The National Autistic Society (2014).
Sex education and children and young people with an ASD
www.autism.org.uk/sexeducation

National Children's Bureau (2014). *Sex Education Forum* **www.sexeducationforum.org.uk**

Information and support on disability, sex and relationships
Outsiders club: (2014). **www.outsiders.org.uk**

Advice on sexual abuse, sexual offending and learning disabilities
Respond: (2014). **www.respond.org.uk**

A range of further resources for a variety of subjects can be found at **www.autism.org.uk/about-autism/our-publications.**

References

Chatzitheochari. S et al (2014).
Bullying victimisation among disabled children and young people: Evidence from two British longitudinal studies.
London: The Institute of Education

Department for Education (2002). *Bullying: don't suffer in silence.*
London: Department for Education

Hattersley, C. (2013). *Autism: understanding behaviour.*
London: The National Autistic Society

HM Government (2003). *Sexual Offences Act 2003*
www.legislation.gov.uk/ukpga/2003/42/contents
(Accessed: 30 August 2014)

Madders, T. (2010). *You Need To Know.*
London: The National Autistic Society

NSPCC (2014). *Bullying*
www.nspcc.org.uk/preventing-abuse/child-abuse-and-neglect/bullying-and-cyberbullying
(Accessed: 30 August 2014)

Nichols, S., Moravick, G. M. and Tetenbaum, S. P. (2009).
Girls growing up on the autism spectrum: what parents and professionals should know about the pre-teen and teenage years.
London: Jessica Kingsley Publishers

Young Minds (2014). *Mental health statistics*
www.youngminds.org.uk/training_services/policy/mental_health_statistics (Accessed: 16 August 2014)

Notes